M000014393

Around the World of Music

by Warren R. Stevens
illustrated by Larry Day

Harcourt

Orlando   Boston   Dallas   Chicago   San Diego

Visit *The Learning Site!*

www.harcourtschool.com

Hi! I'm Maria. For most of the school year, I live in Miami, Florida, but when summer comes, I live all over the world. You see, I have a very musical family. My mom teaches piano, and my big brother plays trumpet in the high school band. I play flute and a couple of other instruments.

We get to travel because of my dad. He's a conductor with a big orchestra here in Miami. He travels a lot, and when school is out we all travel with him. I love the summertime!

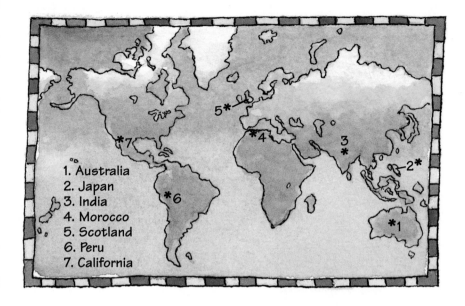

Last summer we went all over the world. We went to Australia, Japan, India, Morocco, Scotland, Peru, and then right back to California in the United States. When we traveled, Dad had to work, but the rest of us could visit different places and hear all sorts of unusual music. I'm always interested in music I haven't heard before. You can never tell when you might learn something that will help you play better. My goal is to be good enough to play in my dad's orchestra.

Dad and Mom both say that I'm pretty close to achieving my goal already. Since I learned so much from all those musicians around the world, I should be good enough in no time.

Every chance I get, I practice. Usually I play unaccompanied, but sometimes Mom or my brother plays with me. Here's a picture of Mom at the piano in the lobby of a hotel we stayed in last summer. Can you believe it? That's me playing in the hotel lobby! It was the only place where both of us could practice.

Practice is really important in learning to play well. I also learned from my parents that it's important to get out and hear other people play. That was easy to do with Mom free to show us around. I couldn't believe how many friends she seemed to have all over the world. Mom says that music makes friends.

One of the first places we visited during our summer trip was Australia. Dad stayed in Sydney most of the trip. His orchestra performed in the fantastic Opera House there in the harbor. The roof of the Opera House looks like the sails of ships. When I first saw it, I couldn't believe it. The sails were full of wind, and it looked as if the Opera House might push off and sail right across the harbor.

We stayed in Sydney for a few days and looked around the city. Three days after we got there, Mom said we should go take a look at the wild places in Australia. That sounded interesting but a little scary.

The native people of Australia have an instrument that is a little like a flute, but it makes quite a different sound. It sounds like a cross between an echo and an insect's hum. It was a real novelty. I had never heard anything like it. I really enjoyed the music because it had a strong beat and a great sound.

Mom said the man who played this instrument was a friend of Dad's. When she introduced me to the man, I told him that I played the flute. He said that we could learn a lot from each other and asked me to play something. I went to the car and got my flute. When I started playing, he joined me. Then he changed the beat and I followed along. Soon we were making brand new music. You wouldn't believe how exciting it was.

After we returned to Sydney and picked Dad up, we went on to Japan. The first night we went to the concert hall to watch Dad and listen to the orchestra. That night an old, thin Japanese man came out onto the stage to perform. I had never seen him before.

I asked Mom who he was. She said that he was the soloist for the night. He would play unaccompanied for part of the concert. His instrument was like the one I had seen in Australia, but it had finger holes and a mouthpiece. It looked like the recorder I had at home.

The music he played was deep and sweet. The sound was a little bit like a recorder's sound, but much deeper. I listened carefully. The music wasn't like the music I played; instead, it seemed to flow like water and sound like the wind. Sometimes there were long pauses between the notes. I sat there, leaning forward in my seat, waiting for the next note. When it came, I almost sighed with relief.

Bamboo flute

When I went backstage after the concert to tell Dad how much I enjoyed it, I met the man with the flute. I asked him to tell me about his instrument. He said that it was made from bamboo. I was surprised when he told me that bamboo is a kind of grass. He said that this was an ancient Japanese instrument.

I wanted to know about all the pauses between the notes. He smiled and told me that silence was the space that music is wrapped around. I thought about that for a long time, but I don't think I really understand it. I *do* know that thinking about it has helped me pay more attention to the quiet parts in my music.

Our next stop was India. I have to admit that I was a little bit afraid to go there. I had heard about earthquakes and floods. I guess I thought they happened all the time over there. They don't.

We went to several cities in India. I had no idea that the country was so large and that so many people lived there. Everywhere we went there were crowds of people.

Some of the cities had street markets and arcades where vendors sold everything from spices to beautiful fabrics. Some of these places had food that smelled so good my mouth watered.

At one market in New Delhi, I saw a snake charmer play. He had a long instrument that was like a recorder or a bamboo flute. The sound it made was much sharper, though. It almost hurt my ears.

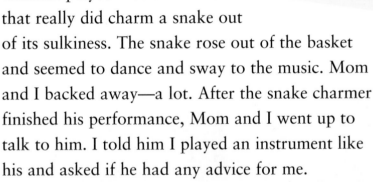

Mom and I watched as the snake charmer played music that really did charm a snake out of its sulkiness. The snake rose out of the basket and seemed to dance and sway to the music. Mom and I backed away—a lot. After the snake charmer finished his performance, Mom and I went up to talk to him. I told him I played an instrument like his and asked if he had any advice for me.

I will never forget what he said. He smiled at me and said, "Oh yes, I do. Always play as though your life depended on it." Then he laughed. So did Mom and I, although we were a bit nervous with the snake there and all.

After visiting about seven different places in India, we were on our way to Morocco.

Like India, the cities in Morocco had many arcades with booths selling all sorts of things. I saw a lot of leather goods—wallets, purses, book covers, things that looked like plates, and even some things that looked like musical instruments. In some of the booths, I saw shiny brass coffeepots and plates.

Mom and I did a lot of shopping and a lot of listening. Everyone in Morocco seemed to have musical instruments. I saw hand-held drums, little brass finger cymbals, and many different stringed instruments.

The instrument I liked best was, of course, a flute. It was about as long as my flute, and the man who played it held it out in front of him instead of to the side the way I play my flute. Mom and I first heard the flutist as we were walking up a wide street leading to a gate that looked out to the desert. He was standing near the gate, playing his flute unaccompanied. Several other musicians were standing nearby.

At first the music was slow and quiet. Little by little it became louder and wilder as first one musician and then another joined in. It was great to hear this amazing music and to see the wind blowing the sands of the desert just behind the little group.

When they finished playing, I asked the man how he was able to play such beautiful music. He smiled at me and pointed to the desert. "When you have beauty like this, it is not hard to play well," he said.

Later, when I thought about it, I was certain he was right.

That same night we flew to Scotland. Scotland was a nice change after the heat and intense sunlight of a desert country like Morocco.

Dad was invited to conduct the Royal Guard of Glasgow. This is a group of about 100 musicians. Their only instruments were bagpipes and drums.

If you haven't ever seen a bagpipe, just imagine an octopus with stiff legs. The legs stick out all over. To play the instrument, you pump on the body of the octopus and blow in through one of the legs. A bagpipe is really strange to look at, but it makes a sound like that of the Indian flute mixed with the Australian instrument.

Dad had a great time conducting, and we all really enjoyed the concert. When they were finished playing, they asked if I would like to join them. Of course I was very excited. I played a little bit of a song I had learned in school called "Loch Lomond."

Our next stop was near the roof of the world. We went to the city of Lima, Peru, high in the Andes Mountains. There I saw the funniest thing of the entire trip—a dancing llama.

One of the men leading the llama was dancing to the music of Andean pipes—and the llama was dancing with him. It was hilarious!

Afterward, we talked to the musician and learned that Andean pipes are made of a row of

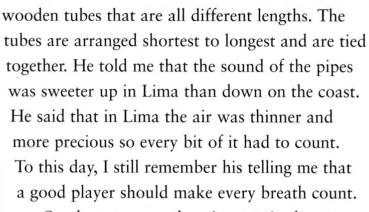

wooden tubes that are all different lengths. The tubes are arranged shortest to longest and are tied together. He told me that the sound of the pipes was sweeter up in Lima than down on the coast. He said that in Lima the air was thinner and more precious so every bit of it had to count. To this day, I still remember his telling me that a good player should make every breath count.

Our last stops on the trip were in the state of California. We started in San Diego, where we went to a small section of town that was filled with very old buildings.

There was a big open patio there, and standing near a fountain was a group of musicians getting ready to play. They all had guitars, and one of them also had what looked like Andean pipes strapped around his neck.

They spent a few minutes adjusting their instruments. Then, with a little flourish, the man with the pipes pulled a scarf from his pocket and let it fall. As it fell, the music started and the crowd cheered.

Later, at a street fair in Los Angeles, we saw more instruments—Indian flutes, bamboo flutes, and even Andean pipes.

When I practice my flute now, I think of all the things those great musicians told me. I pay attention to the quiet parts of the music. I play as if my life depended on it, and it makes the music sweeter. I look at beautiful things, and it helps me understand how much music there is all around me. When I begin to hear it, I just play better.

I hope that you will come and hear me play when you get a chance. I love my flute, and I love music. I think you will be able to tell that when you listen to me play. Someday I want to play my flute for the whole world. Maybe I'll be part of my dad's orchestra.